NEUGEBAUER PRESS LONDON, BOSTON

COPYRIGHT © 1982, VERLAG NEUGEBAUER PRESS, SALZBURG, AUSTRIA
ORIGINAL TITLE: PHILIPP UND DIE SPRINGSCHNUR
COPYRIGHT © 1982, ENGLISH EDITIONS, NEUGEBAUER PRESS U.S.A.INC., BOSTON
PUBLISHED IN U.S.A. BY NEUGEBAUER PRESS U.S.A.INC.,
DISTRIBUTION BY ALPHABET PRESS, BOSTON.
DISTRIBUTION IN CANADA BY GROLIER LTD., TORONTO.
PUBLISHED IN U.K. BY NEUGEBAUER PRESS PUBLISHING LTD., LONDON.
DISTRIBUTION BY A&C BLACK, LONDON.
ALL RIGHTS RESERVED
PRINTED IN AUSTRIA
ISBN O 907234 20 8

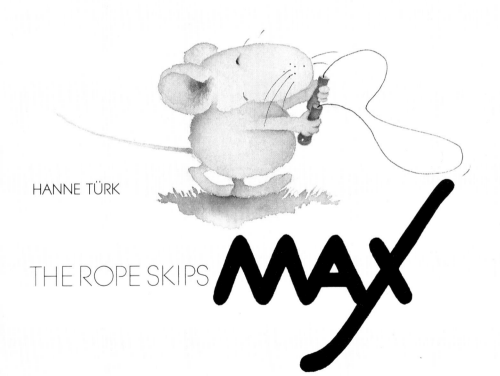

HANNE TÜRK

THE ROPE SKIPS **MAX**